MINDFULNESS
COLOR BY NUMBERS

MINDFULNESS
COLOR BY NUMBERS

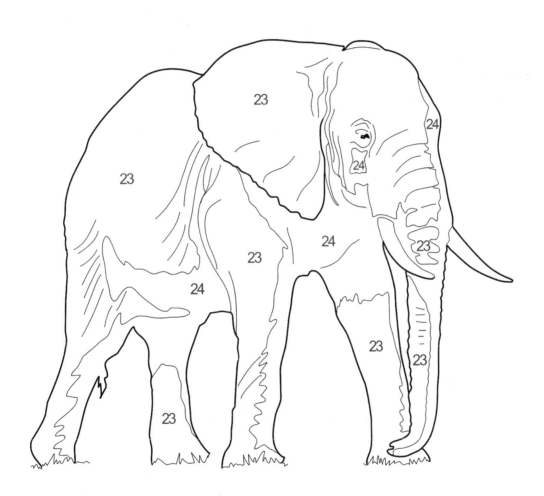

ARCTURUS

ARCTURUS

This edition published in 2019 by Arcturus Publishing Limited
26/27 Bickels Yard, 151–153 Bermondsey Street,
London SE1 3HA

ISBN: 978-1-78950-048-6
CH006903NT

Printed in China

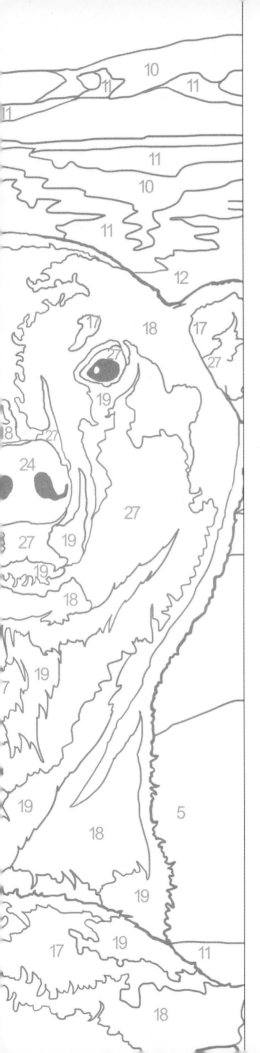

INTRODUCTION

Taking time to reflect on our lives and the wonderful planet on which we live is essential to our well-being, and this beautiful collection of color-by-number images provides an enjoyable and relaxing way to slow down and escape the pressures of everyday life.

The pictures chosen include intricate geometric circles and swirling kaleidoscopes as well as wonderful scenes from nature, such as a tropical beach, snow-capped mountains, and rolling countryside.

The wonderful thing about the compositions in this book is that the work has been done for you—you don't even need to worry about choosing colors. All the images are numbered, and the numbers correspond to the color key on the back cover flap. Match your pencils as closely as possible to the colors in the key—you can even label the pencils with numbers to make things easier. If there is no number, that means the space should be left white or colored with a white pencil.

From mesmerizing mandalas to a walk in the country and animals galore, the book guarantees relaxation and mindfulness while celebrating the beauty, geography, and nature of the world around us.

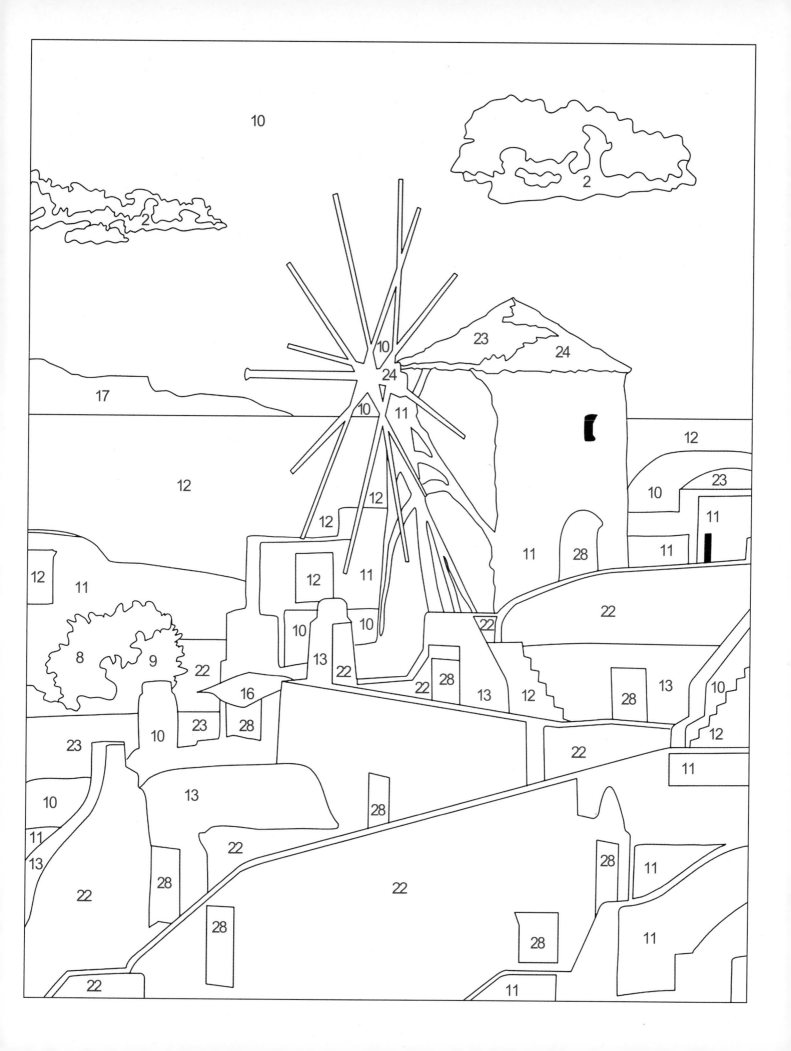

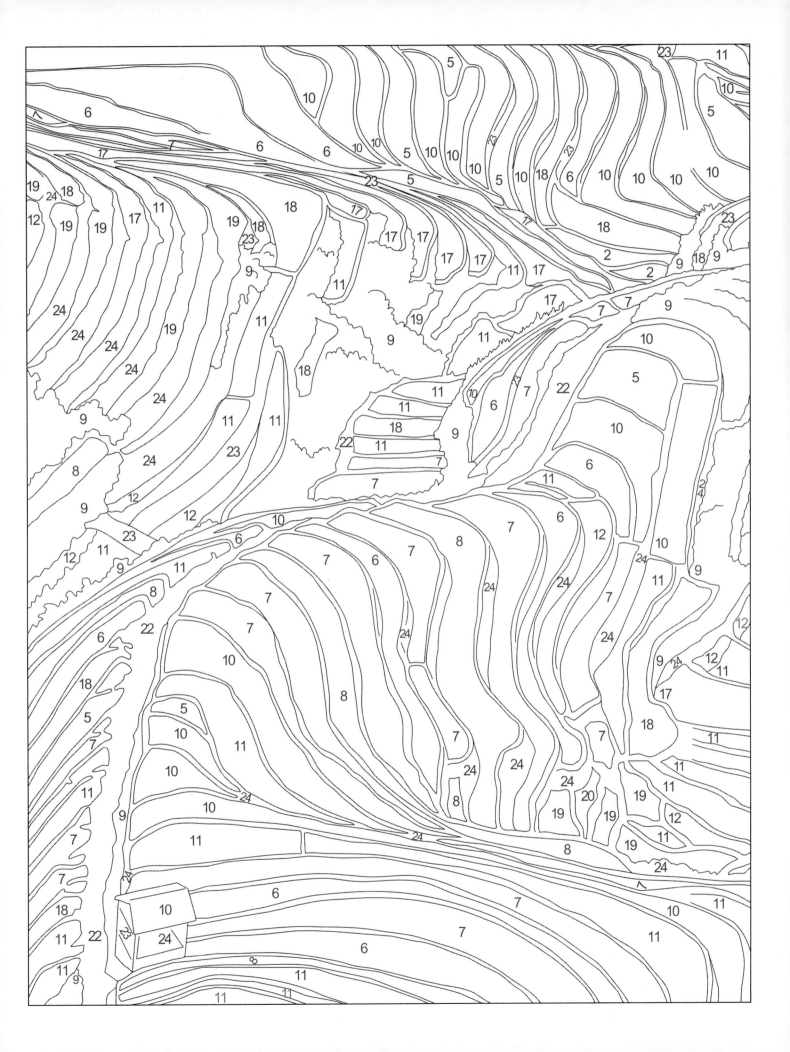